ILLUMINATION PRESENTS

MEGA STICKER BOOK

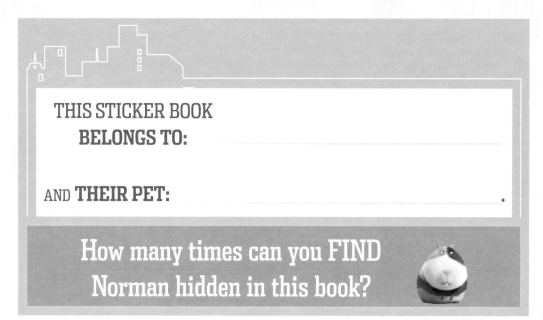

THIS STICKER BOOK
BELONGS TO: _____

AND **THEIR PET:** _____.

How many times can you FIND
Norman hidden in this book?

THE SECRET LIFE OF PETS: **MEGA STICKER BOOK**
A CENTUM BOOK 9781910916513
Published in Great Britain by Centum Books Ltd
This edition published 2016
© 2016 Universal Studios Licensing LLC.
13 5 7 9 10 8 6 4 2

Centum Books Ltd, 20 Devon Square, Newton Abbot, Devon, TQ12 2HR, UK
books@centumbooksltd.co.uk
CENTUM BOOKS Limited Reg. No. 07641486
A CIP catalogue record for this book is available from the British Library
Printed in China.

centum

LET'S MEET THE PETS!

All these pets live in an apartment block in New York City.
Use your stickers to match the pets to their shadows.

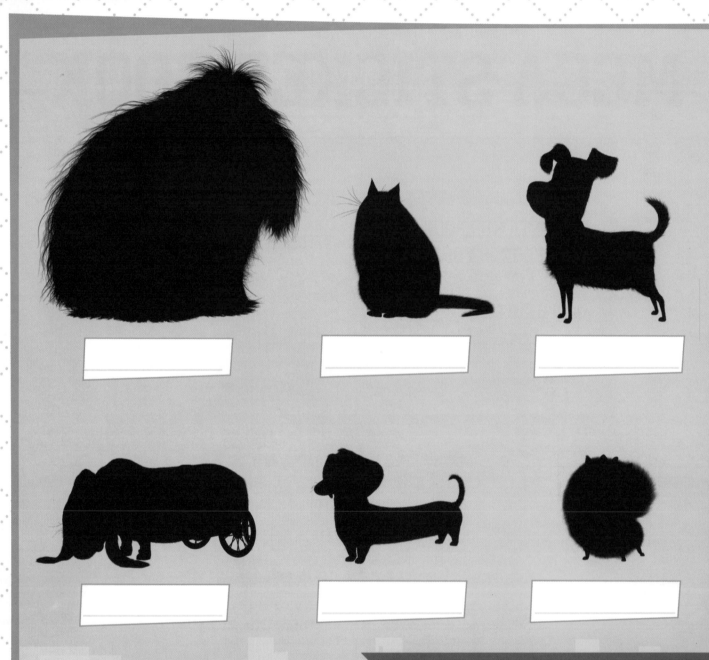

WHO'S A GOOD DOG?
For **extra** brownie points, write each pet's name under their shadow, too.

HOME IS WHERE YOUR PET IS

Each image below is a window into an apartment. Write the name of the pet who lives in each apartment on the line below.

1

2

3

4

5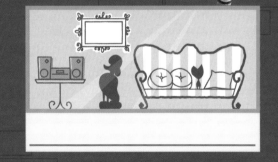

6

HINT: Look closely through each window for a clue.

Answers on page 32

HELLO, MAX!

Max likes nothing more than his owner, Katie . . . well, maybe sausages. Max and Katie are soulmates; everything is perfect, until Katie brings a new 'brother' home . . .

FACT FILE

NAME: Max

OWNER: Katie

BREED: Terrier mix

LIKES: Katie

Stick Max here!

MOST LIKELY TO "BARK!":
"I've got big plans for today. I'm going to sit here and wait for Katie to come back."

WRITE **Max's** name on his collar.

Max has the PERFECT relationship with his owner . . . but he has NO idea why she leaves every day!

Draw a delicious bone for Max in his bowl.

max

WHERE'S MAX'S DOG TAG?

Can you find your way through this maze of dog tags to reunite Max with his dog tag?

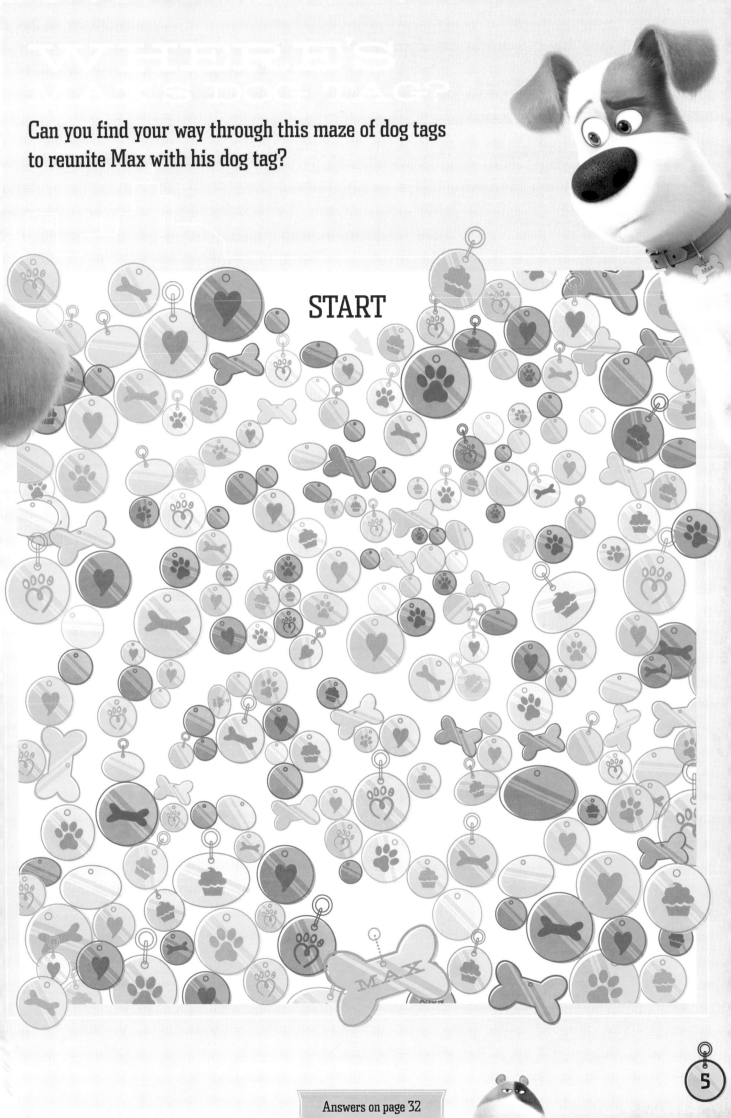

START

MAX

MEET DUKE!

When Katie brings Duke home from the dog pound, he thinks he's found a loving new home. Instead, a rivalry begins ...

FACT FILE

NAME: Duke

OWNER: Katie

BREED: Mutt

LIKES: Sausages

MOST LIKELY TO "BARK!":

"If it's gonna come down to you or me, it's gonna be me."

Stick Duke here!

COLOUR IN **Duke!**

A *BIG*, fuzzy Mutt of a dog who deep down has an *EVEN* BIGGER heart.

FILL this bowl with enough food for massive **Duke!**

When you're a big dog, it can be difficult to check if something or someone is beneath you before you sit down. Use your stickers to complete the puzzle and find out who Duke is sat on.

Duke is sitting on _____.

HELLO, GIDGET!

Gidget is a fluffy white dog who lives in the apartment across from Max. Don't tell anyone, but she has a soft spot for Max.

FACT FILE

NAME: Gidget

BREED: Pomeranian

LIKES: Max

MOST LIKELY TO "BARK!":
"If you find Max, I'll be your best friend."

COLOUR IN **Gidget's** bow.

Stick Gidget here!

50% fluff, 110% TOUGH!

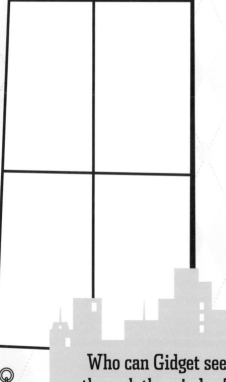

Who can Gidget see through the window?

GIDGET'S HANDBAG

Gidget doesn't get out much, but when she does she likes to go out in **style**! Doodle and colour this handbag for Gidget.

MEET CHLOE!

Chloe is a cat who loves nothing more than food . . . although she isn't so keen on her cat food! She also loves the fridge – especially if it's open.

FACT FILE

NAME: Chloe

BREED: Cat

LIKES: Cake, chicken . . . any human food

MOST LIKELY TO "MIAOW!":
"Dog people are weird."

Stick Chloe here!

Great at GIVING advice but DOESN'T CARE about your problems.

Decorate this cupcake with yummy icing for Chloe.

DRAW a toy for Chloe.

MAZE
THROUGH THE
FRIDGE

Chloe has her eye on that delicious cake. Can you help her find her way through the fridge maze?

HELLO, BUDDY & MEL!

Buddy is the longest and most sarcastic dog around and Mel is just pug-dorable. Let's learn more about these pets.

Stick Buddy here!

FACT FILE

NAME: Buddy

BREED: Dachshund

LIKES: Back massages

MOST LIKELY TO "BARK!":
"A modern stick device? I would not fetch that. I'm old school."

FIRST to arrive, LAST to leave.

WRITE **Mel** and **Buddy's** names on their tags.

FACT FILE

NAME: Mel

BREED: Pug

LIKES: Chasing squirrels

MOST LIKELY TO "BARK!":
"Nobody likes you, squirrel!"

Stick Mel here!

LADY-KILLER on the inside, DOPEY-PUG on the outside.

12

WALKIES WORDSEARCH

Can you find all these words hidden in the grid below?

MAX • DUKE • SNOWBALL • OZONE • TIBERIUS • POPS • MEL
BUDDY • CHLOE • GIDGET • NORMAN • SWEETPEA • LEONARD

D	O	P	E	T	D	E	K	E	P	O	W	U	P
S	N	W	B	L	L	D	U	M	M	O	U	S	S
Z	A	L	E	N	A	E	D	E	N	P	E	T	E
D	S	N	O	W	B	A	L	L	Z	O	N	E	P
O	H	A	G	T	G	U	T	Y	B	E	R	M	S
M	X	X	S	E	W	E	D	T	P	P	E	A	A
S	P	C	E	G	N	U	A	D	H	O	E	X	P
C	E	L	R	D	T	O	C	E	Y	P	J	T	P
H	T	O	T	I	B	E	R	I	U	S	I	O	T
L	N	O	E	G	V	A	N	M	V	R	E	L	E
O	P	E	T	E	E	P	N	O	A	D	N	S	E
E	S	U	N	K	O	I	P	E	T	N	O	T	W
G	I	G	U	D	G	F	A	B	H	O	Z	G	S
T	H	D	R	A	N	O	E	L	R	E	O	E	M
P	E	T	C	U	T	A	G	L	R	A	B	L	L

How many times can you find
the word 'PET' in the grid?

13

MEET NORMAN & SWEETPEA!

These are the smallest pets in the apartment block. Sweetpea is a fearless budgie and Norman is a guinea pig who has been lost in the vents of the apartment building for quite some time.

FACT FILE

NAME: Norman

BREED: Guinea pig

LIKES: He's forgotten, but he'll know when he sees it

MOST LIKELY TO "SQUEAK!":
"Is this the third or second floor?"

Stick Norman here!

Has the brain the size of a PEA *– only chooses to use* HALF *of it.*

FACT FILE

NAME: Sweetpea

BREED: Budgerigar

LIKES: Actions that require no fear (he has none!)

MOST LIKELY TO: Be practising daring flying tricks

Stick Sweetpea here!

TWO WINGS ONE PRAYER.

SAUSAGE SEQUENCES

For Max and Duke, the best thing to come after a sausage is another sausage.

Can you complete each row?
Use your stickers to add the next SAUSAGE in the sequences.

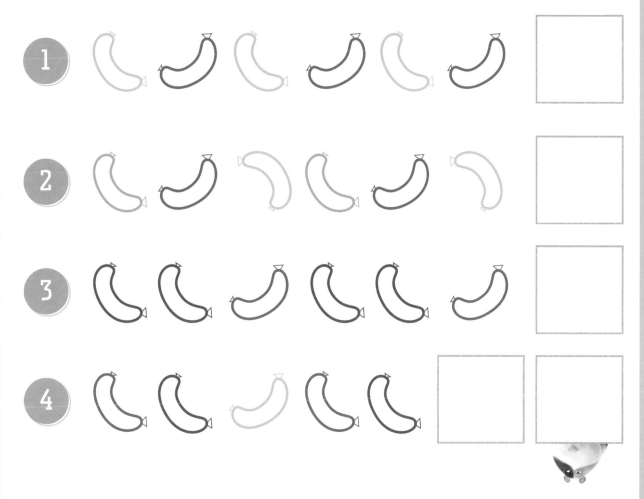

Now make up your OWN sausage sequence.

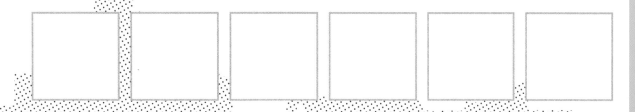

Answers on page 32

HELLO, POPS, TIBERIUS & LEONARD!

The apartment block is full of all sorts of pets: a hawk, an old basset hound with two legs and two wheels, and a punk poodle.

Stick Tiberius here!

COLOUR IN Tiberius.

FACT FILE

NAME: Tiberius

BREED: Red-tailed hawk

LIKES: Small animals (to eat)

MOST LIKELY TO "SQUAWK!":
"I can't help it. I was born with killer instincts."

The ONLY thing sharper than his wit is his talons.

DRAW what you think Tiberius is perched o

He knows the city like the back of his wrinkled paw.

FACT FILE

NAME: Pops

BREED: Basset hound

LIKES: All-day parties when his owner is away (which is always!)

MOST LIKELY TO "BARK!": "These guys are a bit testy. Let me do the talking."

NAME: Leonard

BREED: Poodle

LIKES: Headbanging to heavy rock

MOST LIKELY TO 'BARK': "Let's rock!"

Stick
Leonard here!

Doodle
some music notes around him.

COLOUR IN
Leonard.

There's nothing THIS posh pooch *likes better than* HARD ROCK!

Stick
Pops here!

MEET SNOWBALL!

NAME: SNOWBALL

BREED: RABBIT

LIVES: IN THE UNDERBELLY

MOST LIKELY TO SAY:
"LIBERATED FOREVER! DOMESTICATED NEVER!"

THIS WHITE, FLUFFY BUNNY IS THE LEADER OF THE FLUSHED PETS. HE'S INSANELY CUTE . . . BUT ALSO INSANE. LET'S GET TO KNOW THIS BUNNY AND EXACTLY WHO WE'RE DEALING WITH!

STICK SNOWBALL HERE!

THE PASSWORD TO GET INTO THE UNDERBELLY IS:
"DON'T ASK THE LEADER FOR THE PASSWORD".

WHICH MOOD DO YOU THINK SNOWBALL IS IN HERE?

DRAW A CARROT IN SNOWBALL'S PAW.

THE MOODS OF SNOWBALL

SNOWBALL'S MOODS ARE CHANGEABLE IN A MOMENT – AND THIS CAN BE DANGEROUS! USE THE LINES BELOW TO MATCH EACH PICTURE OF SNOWBALL TO HIS MOOD. HE'S A TRICKY BUNNY, SO THERE'S A LETTER TO HELP YOU.

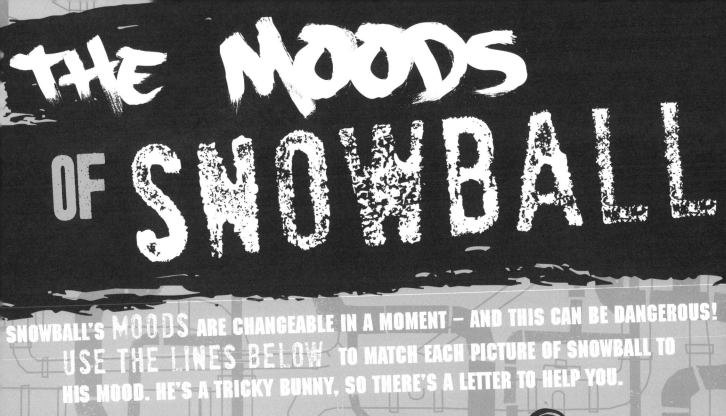

A. X _ _ _ _

B. _ P _ _ _

C. _ _ Z _

HAPPY   ANGRY   EXCITED   UPSET   CRAZY

D. _ P _ _ _

E. N _ _ _ _

F. WRITE HOW YOU THINK SNOWBALL IS FEELING HERE BELOW:

WHEN YOU'VE MATCHED ALL SNOWBALL'S MOODS, ADD A **CARROT STICKER** HERE.

ANSWERS ON PAGE 32

MEET THE FLUSHED PETS

THIS GANG OF PETS RUNS THE STREETS OF NEW YORK – THEY DO NOT ANSWER TO OWNERS BECAUSE THEY DON'T HAVE THEM! MATCH EACH SHADOW TO THE CORRECT CHARACTER STICKER.

xxxo

OZONE LIKES TO KEEP THINGS ON A NEED-TO-KNOW BASIS, SO HE HAS TO KEEP HIS MESSAGES IN CODE. CAN YOU HELP HIM CRACK THIS CODE USING THE DECODER BELOW?

V C A W N Q J W Z   S B N W I W N !

_ _ _ _ _ _ _ _ _   _ _ _ _ _ _ _ !

Z B T W U J C X Q J W Z   G W I W N !

_ _ _ _ _ _ _ _ _ _ _ _   _ _ _ _ _ !

WHO SAID THIS PHRASE?

_ _ _ _ _ _ _ _ _ _

xxx

THE DECODER

A	B	C	D	E	F	G	H	I	J	K	L	M	N	O	P	Q	R	S	T	U	V	W	X	Y	Z
Q	A	X	Z	W	S	E	D	C	R	F	V	T	G	B	Y	H	N	U	J	M	I	K	O	L	P

HELLO, TATTOO!

NAME: TATTOO

BREED: POT-BELLIED PIG

ROLE IN FLUSHED PETS:
MAP READER, TAXI THIEF

FACT ABOUT TATTOO:
HIS OLD OWNER WAS A TATTOO ARTIST
. . . AND PRACTISED ON TATTOO

MOST LIKELY TO "OINK!":
"THEY SAY EVERYONE'S GOING TO
BROOKLYN THESE DAYS."

HE'S A POT-BELLIED PIG
WHO IS COVERED IN BODY ART.

STICK
TATTOO
HERE!

COLOUR IN
TATTOO.

DESIGN A NEW
TATTOO FOR
TATTOO HERE.

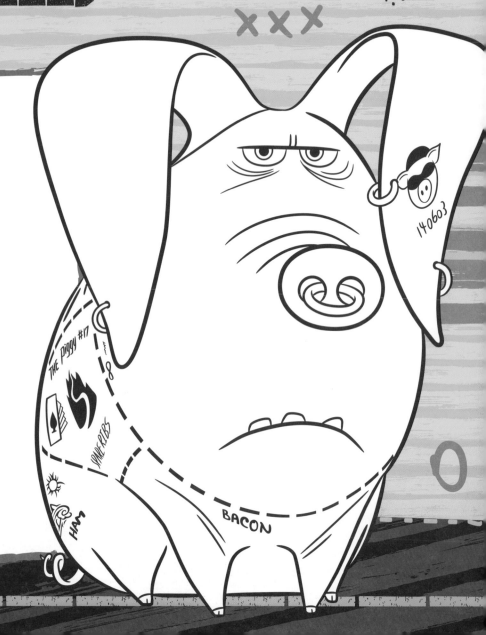

22

COUNT TATTOO'S TATTOOS

TATTOO HAS MANY TATTOOS . . . IT'S HOW HE GOT HIS NAME!
HOW MANY TATTOOS CAN YOU COUNT ON TATTOO?

TATTOO HAS ☐ TATTOOS.

ANSWERS ON PAGE 32

HELLO, OZONE!

OZONE IS AN ALLEY CAT WITH AN ATTITUDE . . . A BAD ATTITUDE! HE MIGHT LOOK VERY UGLY ON THE OUTSIDE, BUT HE'S ALSO VERY UGLY ON THE INSIDE.

NAME: OZONE

BREED: ALLEY CAT

ROLE:
LEADER OF THE ALLEY CATS

FACT ABOUT OZONE:
HIS ALLEY CAT SECOND-IN-COM-MAND IS CALLED NITRO

MOST LIKELY TO "MIAOW!":
"I'D WATCH YOUR TONE, SUNSHINE."

STICK OZONE HERE!

DRAW OZONE'S ALLEY CAT GANG.

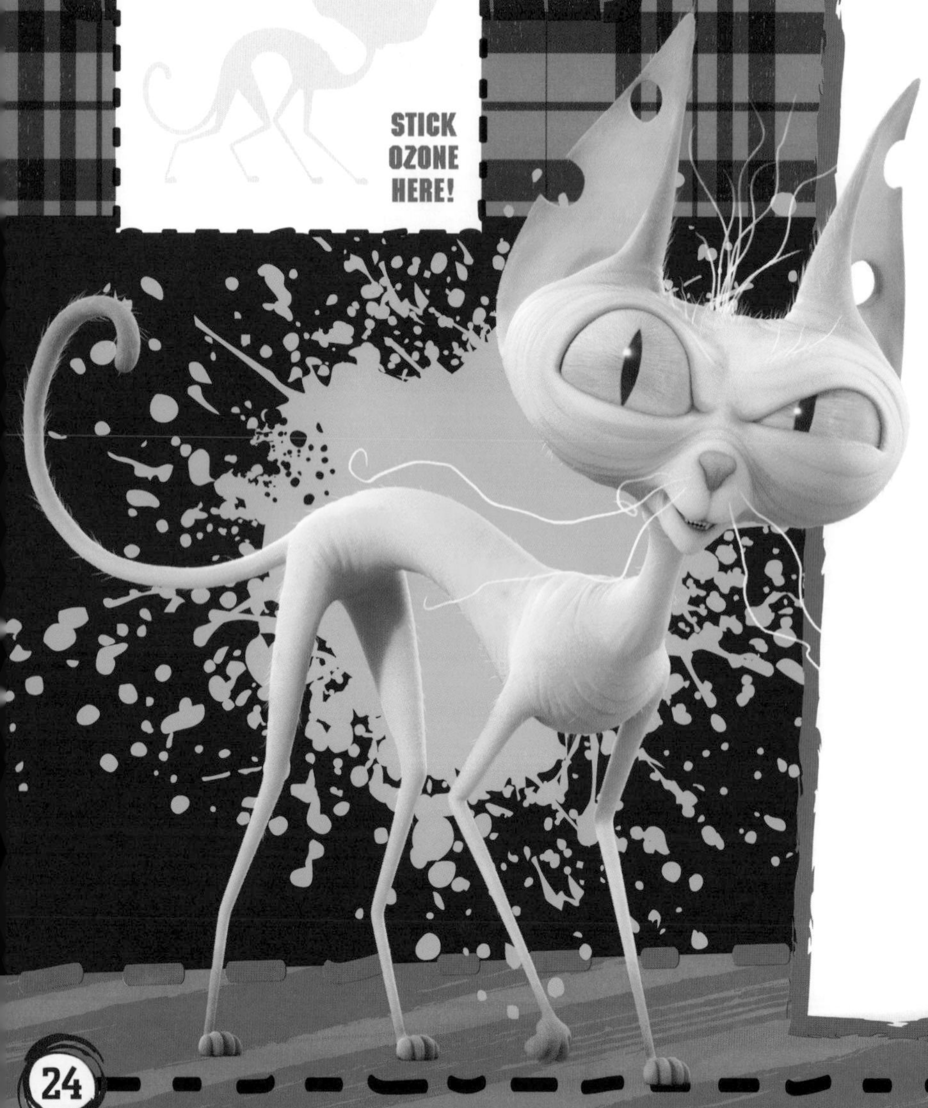

CLOTHES LINES, CATS AND CHAOS!

MAX IS TRYING TO HIDE FROM OZONE. CAN YOU HELP GUIDE OZONE THROUGH THE CLOTHES LINE MAZE TO FIND MAX'S HIDING PLACE?

HOW MANY CATS' SHADOWS CAN YOU COUNT?

FINISH

START

ANSWERS ON PAGE 32

25

HELLO, DERICK, RIPPER AND DRAGON!

THESE FLUSHED PETS ARE SNOWBALL'S MUSCLE.

NAME: RIPPER

BREED: BULLDOG

ROLE IN THE FLUSHED PETS:
TRANSPORT FOR SNOWBALL, PUSHCHAIR THIEF

FACT ABOUT RIPPER:
HE OFTEN FINDS HIMSELF BEING CAUGHT BY THE DOG CATCHER

STICK RIPPER HERE!

NO BARK JUST BITE

COLOUR IN RIPPER.

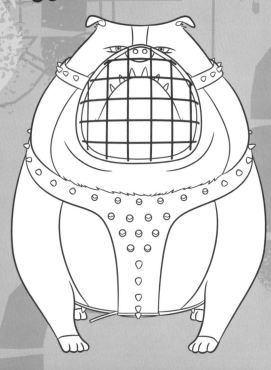

HE IS COLD-BLOODED
. . . LITERALLY

COLOUR IN DRAGON.

NAME: DRAGON

ANIMAL: LIZARD

ROLE IN THE FLUSHED PETS:
DRIVER, TAXI THIEF

FACT ABOUT DRAGON:
HE CAN CRAWL UP ANY WALL AND ACROSS CEILINGS

STICK DRAGON HERE!

STICK
DERICK
HERE!

NAME: DERICK

ANIMAL: CROCODILE

ROLE IN THE FLUSHED PETS:
TO STAND THERE AND LOOK
TERRIFYING – A JOB HE WAS BORN TO DO!

COLOUR IN
DERICK.

SNOWBALL'S
SCALY MUSCLE

DRAW A
NEW RECRUIT
TO THE
FLUSHED PETS.

HOW MANY SEWER PIPES?

OH, NO! MAX IS LOST IN THE SEWERS. HOW MANY SEWER PIPES CAN YOU COUNT BELOW?

HOW MANY OF THE SEWER PIPES ARE RED?

WELCOME TO THE UNDERBELLY!

COLOUR IN SNOWBALL IN THE UNDERBELLY. DRAW IN SOME MORE SNAKES TO CREATE A SNAKE GATE!

TEST YOUR KNOWLEDGE

How much have you learnt about all the *Pets* in this book?
TAKE THIS QUIZ TO FIND OUT!

1. What is the name of Max and Duke's owner?

 **a.** Gidget   **b.** Jane    **c.** Gemma    **d.** Katie

2. How many legs does Pops have?

 a. two    **b.** three   **c.** nine   **d.** four

3. Who is this?

4. What colour is Snowball?

 **a.** white   **b.** grey    **c.** black   **d.** pink

5. Who has a crush on Max?

 **a.** Snowball    **b.** Chloe    **c.** Gidget   **d.** Duke

6. What sort of music does Leonard like most?

 **a.** hard rock    **b.** classical    **c.** pop    **d.** polka

7. Which pet is lost in the apartment vents?

 **a.** Sweetpea   **b.** Leonard    **c.** Ozone   **d.** Norman

8. There are two pets who can fly. Doodle one of them below.

How did you do?

0–3 Oh dear! Were you distracted by a . . . Oh, is that a ball?

4–6 Good try! Perhaps read back over the questions you got wrong.

7–8 Who's a good dog? You are! (Even if you're not a dog!)

31

Answers on page 32

ANSWERS

PAGE 3
1) Chloe, 2) Max, 3) Sweetpea,
4) Buddy, 5) Leonard, 6) Gidget.

PAGE 5

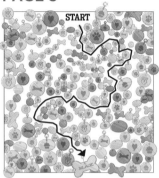

PAGE 7
Duke is sitting on Max.

PAGE 11

PAGE 13

PAGE 15

PAGE 19
A) EXCITED, B) HAPPY, C) CRAZY,
D) UPSET, E) ANGRY

PAGE 21
Snowball said - LIBERATED FOREVER!
DOMESTICATED NEVER!

PAGE 23
Tattoo has 44 tattoos.

PAGE 25

There are 17
cat's shadows.

PAGE 28
There are 25 sewer pipes. 8 are red.

PAGE 30–31
1) d, 2) a, 3) Dragon, 4) a, 5) c, 6) a, 7) d.
8) Sweetpea and Tiberius can fly.

Did you FIND all the hidden Normans in this book?

PAGE 10

PAGE 12

PAGE 14

PAGE 15

PAGE 16

PAGE 20

PAGE 17

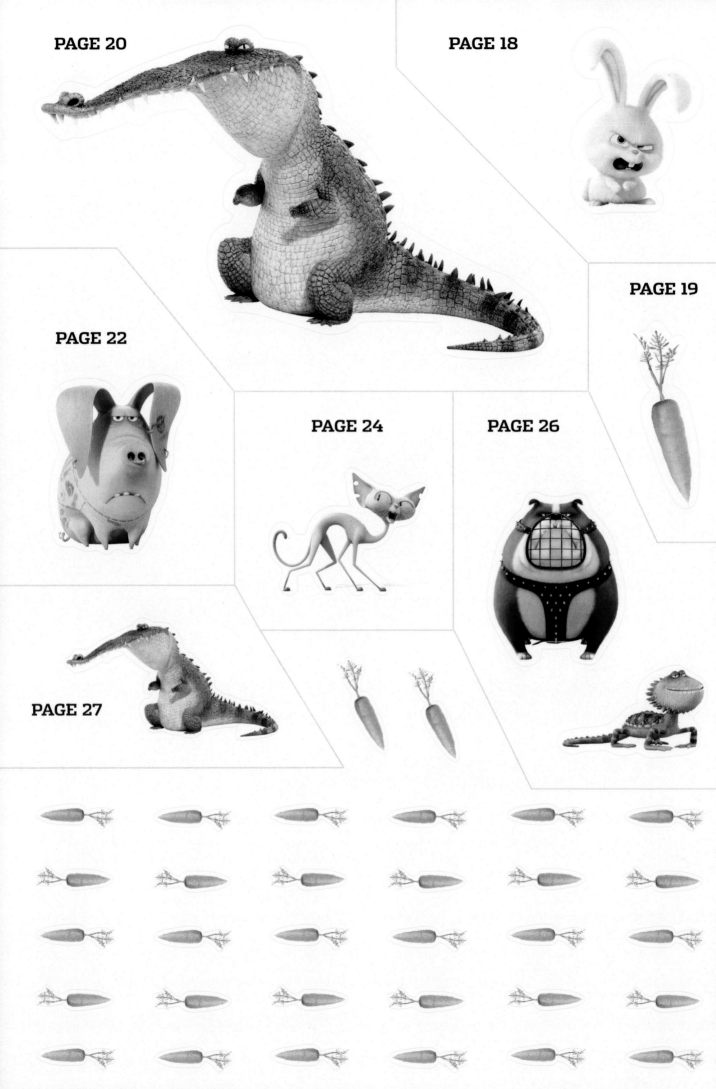

PAGE 20

PAGE 18

PAGE 19

PAGE 22

PAGE 24

PAGE 26

PAGE 27

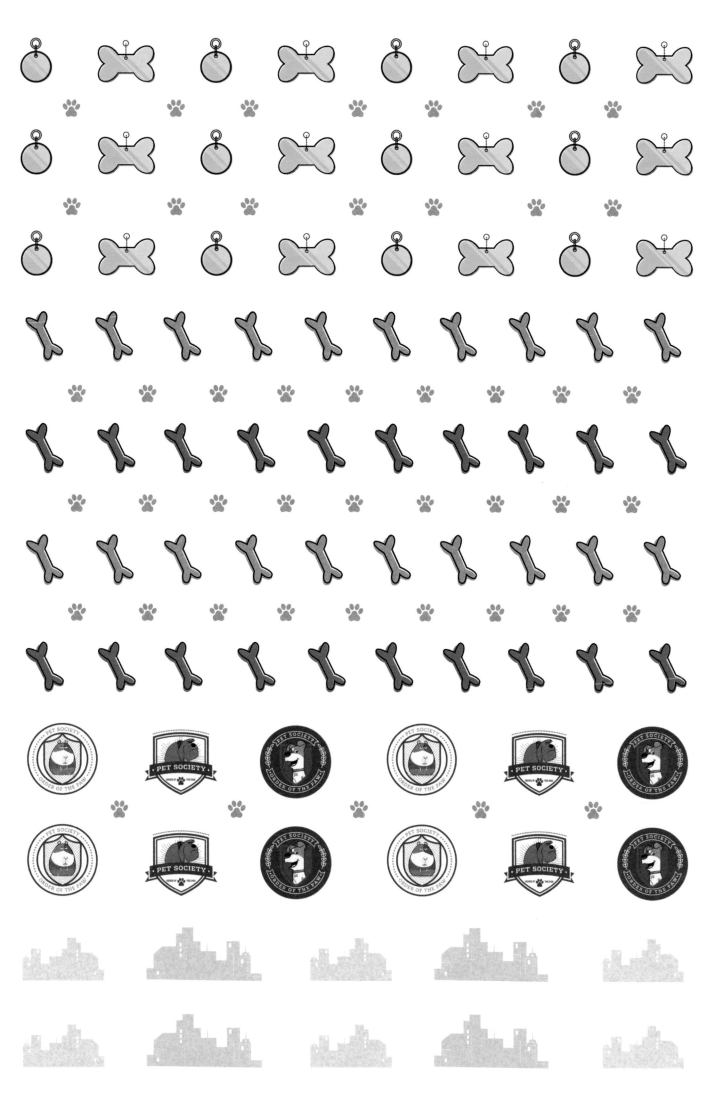

ATTITUDE TO SPARE

THIS IS MY HAPPY FACE

QUINTESSENTIAL BAD DOG

OBEY THE BUNNY

OBEY THE BUNNY